VIEWS
from
THE
BEN

First published in Great Britain

By Kessock Books 2015

A CIP catalogue record for this book is available from the British Library

ISBN 978-0-9930296-2-2

Printed by FTRR Printers,

60 Grant Street,

Inverness, IV3 8BS

A Clarty Wee Boorach of a Book

By

Rab MacWilliam

Kessock Books 2015

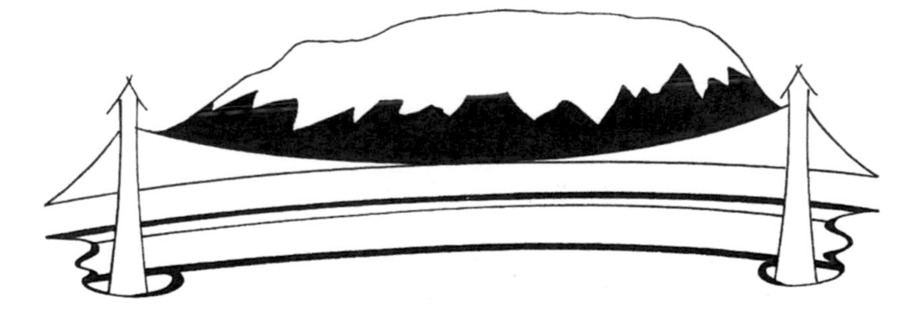

INTRODUCTION

The title of this book - *Views from the Ben* - is quite straightforward, and is in a similar style to our previous title *Snow on the Ben: A guide to the 'Real' Inverness and Highlands.* The 'Ben' in both cases is Ben Wyvis in Ross and Cromarty which can easily be seen from Inverness and which acts as a guide to the changing seasons.

But the subtitle: 'A clarty wee boorach of a book'? What the hell does that mean? If you're an Invernessian, you'll understand it immediately. If not, I can do no better than quote from my definitions in *Snow on the Ben*, as follows:

Clarty: used south of Daviot but also a common Inverness word. Means 'dirty' or 'muddy'. Most frequently used by parents when their wee darlings spill food on their clothes or dirty their knees playing football or skipping or whatever kids do these days. Not nasty or unpleasant, just 'messy'. 'Och, away and wash yersel, ye wee clart'.

Boorach (a hard 'ch'): an untidy and unsightly jumble, or an unplanned, confusing or inexplicable set of circumstances. Originates from the Gaelic 'burach', meaning 'a mess'. A term often used by aunties and grannies when they have visitors: 'och, the room's a right old boorach' (although they've spent all morning tidying it up). May also be employed ('a bit of a boorach') when males enact hostile virility rituals outside public houses at closing time, a fairly frequent demonstration of stumbling bravado. It's a handy word generally, as it can be used to describe any unusual behaviour which you can't be bothered to explain: 'och, it was jist a boorach'.

I expect that this leaves you none the wiser about the contents of *Views from the Ben*, and if we were to describe the book as 'eccentric', we could perhaps be accused of over-simplification.

The book began life as an entertaining, if somewhat different, quiz book on Inverness and the surrounding area. However, as we we were inventing and compiling the questions, we increasingly felt that these tests of your knowledge may benefit from an irreverent diversion or two. So we started adding a few illustrations and jokes. Well, why not? Our powers of recall need a rest from time to time.

Then we decided that, as we had already deviated from our original brief, we may as well include other subjects, purely to maintain your interest. So we began to intersperse the material with a few brief biographies of interesting but often unheralded Highland characters.

To confuse the matter still further, and for no real reason other than that you may enjoy reading it, we compiled, and again interspersed throughout the book, what we call a 'Cheuchter Top Ten' songs listing which is virtually impossible to describe, other than as unique. We welcome your suggestions for other songs, in a similar vein, which you feel may be worthy of inclusion in future edition.

By this point we realised that. as all books have to end somewhere, then so should this one. So we reined in our enthusiasms, stopped writing, and what you are currently holding in your hands is the result of these musings. But the core of the book remains the quiz. three possible answers of which only one (usually) is correct. In some cases the answers are obvious, while in others they will stimulate your concentration and require some thought (and possibly suspension of disbelief). Naturally, we provide the answers at the foot of each page.

View from the Ben is original in all its foibles and facets, and there is nothing in print quite like it. Our intention is that it will appeal as much to Invernessians in search of an amusing and even informative read as it will to visitors trying to make sense of this complex land of differing landscapes, cultures, dialects, peoples and backgrounds.

So turn to the next page, and off you go. We hope you have as enjoyable a time reading it as we did in its writing.

Right 'enuff.

Rab MacWilliam, London, September 2015

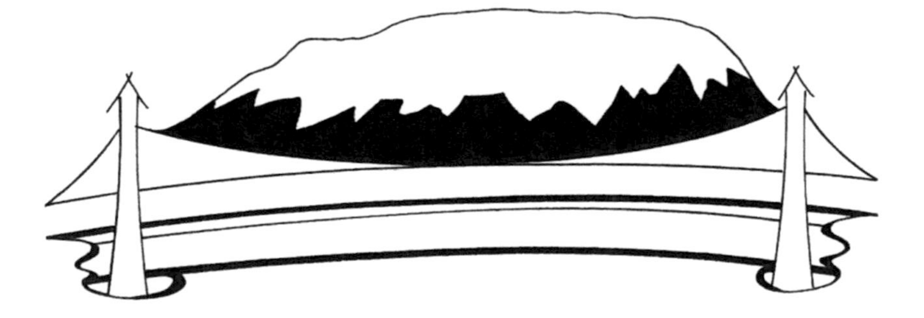

Acknowledgements

Writing this book was like beginning several articles on different subjects all at once, but the reason I hope it will entertain and amuse you is thanks to my friends and Kessock Books co-directors - Mike Clark, George MacWilliam, Brian Urquhart and John Watt - who helped greatly in putting it together. Also, thanks to Merrill MacWilliam, a source of cheerful encouragement in the project, designer of the cover title, and creator of the cartoons in the book, and to my wife Anne Beech for putting up with me **and** my many tantrums and disappearances downstairs. George Murray's assistance was, as ever, invaluable, as was that of Richard, Kevin, Stewart and all the people at FTRR in their design and printing of the book.

I much appreciate the co-operation of Cigarbox Don for allowing us to use his lyrics. I hope that the other popular performers and singers whose lyrics I have slightly rewritten in 'The Cheuchter Top Ten' are in no way offended by this, as my new versions are designed to be a respectful homage to some of my favourite artists and their songs.

Finally, my thanks go to all my friends in the Inverness area and the Highlands generally for being themselves and for remaining the same friendly, kind people they were all those years ago.

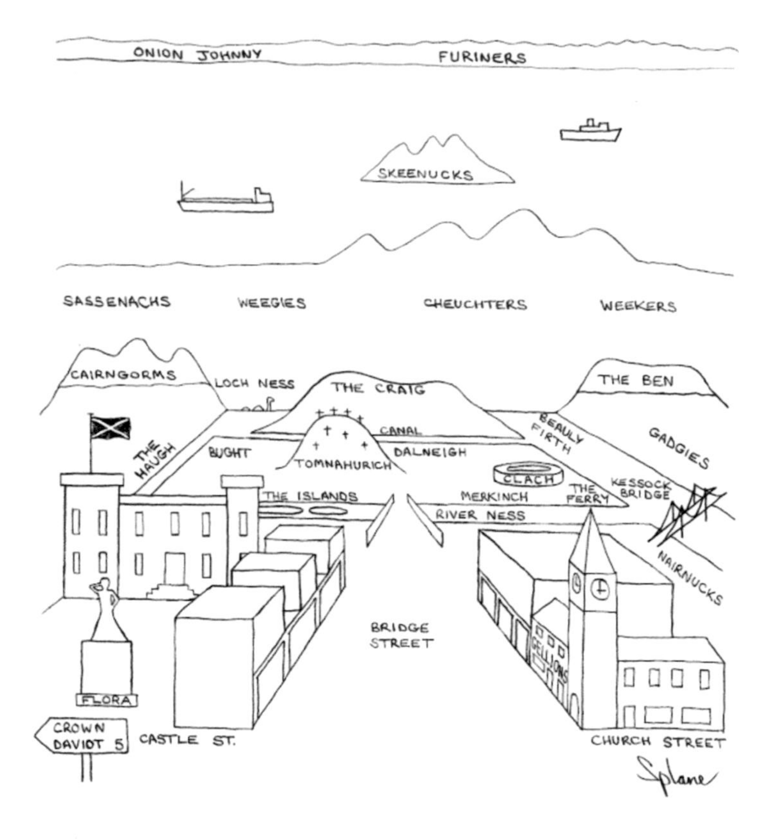

The Invernessian view of the world
By Mike Clark

1)

Q: What is 'Nessie'?

A:

i) A marketing triumph to make people spend money in Inverness

ii) An animal that may or may not inhabit Loch Ness

ii) A ridiculous figment of someone's imagination

1) (Correct: all of them)

Shortly after The Battle of Culloden a search party of fifty Government soldiers was searching for Jacobite fugitives. They were passing through a glen when a hairy Highlander appeared on top of a hill, waving a sword at them.

The Captain said "Corporal, take two men and arrest that savage". The three of them disappear over the hill, and a few minutes later the Highlander re-appears waving his sword. The Captain said "Sergeant, take six men and subdue that savage". Again the men disappear over the hill, and a few minutes later the Highlander re-appears waving his sword.

Exasperated, the Captain says "Lieutenant, take twenty men and kill that savage". The soldiers disappear over the hill, and after a few minutes one of them re-appears at the hilltop, and shouts "it's a trap: there's two of them!".

---

2)
Q: Who or what is Craig Dunain?
A:
i) A Dingwall pop singer from the early 1960s
ii) Cockney rhyming slang for 'insane' ('he went completely Craig Dunain')
iii) A hill to the southwest of Inverness

3)
Q: Who won the Battle of Culloden?
A:
i) Calum Kennedy
ii) The British Hanoverian State
iii) No one. The SNP is still fighting it

2) (Correct: iii)

3) (Correct: ii (or iii))

4)

Q: Where in Inverness did King Macbeth live?

A:

i) With his grannie in Grant Street

ii) In a castle above the Academy Playing Fields

iii) In the back bar of the Gellions

4) (Correct: ii)

Highland Characters: A Highland Visionary

In the 17th century in the Easter Ross area there may or may not have existed a peasant prophet known as the 'Brahan Seer'. Some people dismiss him as an invention, but the probability is that this Highland Nostradamus was a real person who possessed the power of 'second sight' and an uncanny ability to predict the future.

His Gaelic name was Coinneach Odhar Flosaiche, or Kenneth MacKenzie in English, and he was born in Uig in Lewis at the beginning of the 17th century. He lived near Brahan Castle (hence his pseudonym), near Dingwall, where he was employed by the Lord of Seaforth. Legend has it that he used an 'Adder Stone', a stone with a round hole in the middle, to see into the future.

Many of his prophecies were quite remarkable in their accuracy and outcome. Some examples include the following: the construction of the Caledonian Canal ('one day ships will sail round the back of Tomnahurich Hill'); the bridge at Bonar would be swept away by a flood, as happened in 1892; when five bridges were built across the River Ness, a worldwide disaster would follow - the month after the fifth bridge was built, Hitler invaded Poland; a deaf-mute chief of the Clan Mackenzie of Seaforth would mark the end of the clan lineage, as occurred; a battle would be fought on Drumossie Moor, which was the site of the Battle of Culloden; the building of a railway line from Dingwall to Kyle ('long strings of carriages without horses will run between Dingwall and Skye'); and the discovery of North Sea oil ('black rain will bring riches to Aberdeen').

He was murdered at Chanonry Point, on the instructions of Lady Seaforth, by being plunged head first into a barrel of boiling oil. It is unknown whether or not he predicted his own horrifying demise, but the Brahan Seer remains a figure of legend and mystery in the Highlands.

Prophecies of the Brahan Seer

5)

Q: What does the phrase 'cailin ma ruin-sa' suggest to you?

A:

i) 'If I ever hear this again, I'm going to belt someone'

ii) Gaelic for 'Dearest my own one'

iii) 'I don't know. I don't speak Turkish'

6)

Q: What are or were the Clearances?

A:

i) What scaffies do when the bars are shut

ii) The eviction of crofters in the 18th/19th centuries

iii) A new range of Boots skin care cream products

7)

Q: What would happen if you fell in the Caledonian Canal?

A:

i) You'd get wet

ii) You'd find that cow you lost last year

iii) You'd meet several of your old friends you thought were living in Kiltarlity

5) (Correct: ii)

6) (Correct: ii)

7) (Correct: i)

Cheuchter Top Ten

This top ten listing is what we at Kessock Books, and our many supporters and readers, consider to be a collection of some fine popular songs, the lyrics of which we or others have rewritten to reflect the cultural context of the Highlands. The songs are spread throughout the book in reverse order of popularity and we supply the appropriate guitar chords in each case.

We certainly have no intention of denigrating the original versions: rather we see it as our paying homage to some of the great lyricists and performers of our musical age. If you have any favorites which you would like to see included in the next edition, please write to us at kessockbooks.com.

10

Me and Morag MacPhee

Obviously, the source for this re-interpretation is Kris Kristofferson's 'Me and Bobby Magee', written in 1969 and subsequently recorded by Janis Joplin, Grateful Dead et al. Our version and chorus are as follows:

First verse

'(*G*) Busted flat in thon scabby old station square in Tain
Feeling nearly faded as ma (*D*) jeans
(*D7*) Morag thumbed a tractor down, just before Balbain
Took us all the way to Achnasheen (*G*)
I took my pibroch out o' ma smelly Campbell bunnet
And was blowin' hard while (*G7*) Morag sunk a few (*C*)
Wi' the driver swearing at the rain and (*G*) leerin' at ma burd
We sang the (*D*) only Gaelic song that bodach knew (*G*)'

Chorus
(*C*) A turnip's jist another word for a (*G*) scabby little neep
(*D*) Neeps taste (*D7*) disgusting but they're free (*G*)
(*C*) Never buy neeps when you can (*G*) pinch them from the ground
(*D*) At least, that's what Morag said to me (*G*).'

This song is a splendid 'agricultural seduction ballad,' and well worth its place in our chart. The melody sounds Scottish-Irish, like so many US country and folk songs, and it is based on the old habit in the Highlands and elsewhere of 'thumbing a lift', something rarely seen these days. And it's about time that someone wrote a song chorus about neeps. So here it is, at number ten.

8)
Q: What is the meaning of the word 'boke'?
A:
i) The Irish pronounciation of the word 'book'
ii) An internet acronym for 'Bugger Off ye Kilted Eejit'
iii) To be violently ill due to unwise alcohol intake

9)
Q: What was the Duke of Cumberland called after the Battle of Culloden?
A:
i) Bonnie Prince Cumbie
ii) Butcher
iii) Fat English bastard

8) (Correct: iii)
9) (Correct: ii and iii)

A Chinese girl and Englishman met and fell in love. Both were chefs, and they decided to open a Chinese/English 'fusion' restaurant in London. The reviews were good, but the Chinese food made you feel hungry again a half hour after the meal, and the English food meant that you experienced an overwhelming urge to open a darling litle pottery in the Highlands.

---

10)
Q: What are 'silver darlings'?
A:
i) Sporrans packed with brand new 50p coins
ii) Old wifies from Daviot who wink at you in dance halls
iii) Shoals of herring

10) (Correct: iii)

A wifie from Cromarty went out fishing in her husband's rowing boat. She went missing, and some hours later the coastguard called her daughter's house.

The son-in-law answered and was told by his coastguard mate Willie that they found the wifie's body on the far side of the Sutors, but it was in a bad way, with six lobsters attached to it. Willie asked the son-in-law what he should do. The son-in-law said "you keep three, I'll take three, reset her and put her out on the next tide".

Two Cameron Highlanders, Willie and Sandy, were battling away at El Alamein in the blazing desert heat. Sandy said to Willie "what is today's date?" Jimmy said he thought it was the 15th August. Sandy said "it's the Nairn Games today". Willie looked up and said "well, they're getting a grand day for it".

---

11)
Q: What is a 'Wee Free'?
A:
i) A vertically challenged Highland Maoist
ii) A supporter of non-payment for public toilets (sometimes called a 'Free Wee')
iii) A member of the Free Church of Scotland

11) (Correct: iii)

12)
Q: Who or what is a 'boorach'?
A:
i) A white supremacist from South Africa
ii) A churlish cheuchter
iii) An untidy and unsightly jumble, or an unplanned, confusing or inexplicable set of circumstances

13)
Q: Why was the Brahan Seer ('Coinneach Odhar') burnt to death on what is now Fortrose Golf Club?
A:
i) He persuaded people to put their life savings on Ross County to win the European Cup
ii) He missed an easy putt
iii) He predicted the demise of the House of Seaforth

14)
Q: How does one handle the problem of 'midgies'?
A:
i) Chain smoke ten Gauloise at a time while swearing a lot
ii) Blow little kisses at them
iii) Don't go to the west coast of the Highlands in August

12) (Correct: iii)
13) (Correct: iii)
14) (Correct: iii)

Highland Characters: Calum's Road

Determination, single-mindedness and a healthy disdain for authority are traits displayed by many inhabitants of the Highlands, and particularly by those living on the West Coast and the Islands. However, it would be difficult to find a more laudable and praiseworthy example of this thrawn mindset than Calum MacLeod, a crofter and assistant lighthouse keeper on the Isle of Raasay.

Calum had been attempting for years, with no success, to persuade the local authority to build a road from his home in Arnish, in the north of the island, to the ruins of 15th-century Brochel Castle, from where a road began to head southward. Eventually, arming himself with a copy of a book called *Road Making and Maintenance*, a pick, a shovel and a wheelbarrow, he decided to build the road himself.

For ten years, between 1964 and 1974, Calum worked on the road, until he reached his target of Brochel Castle, a distance of just under two miles. During his heroic endeavour, Calum had to negotiate steep climbs and descents, cliffs, rocky inlets and boggy marshland, but this indomitable crofter finally ended his task. The road has become known as 'Calum's Road'.

A few years after the road's completion, the local authority grudgingly succumbed to public pressure and officially adopted and surfaced Calum's Road. Calum was awarded the British Empire Medal, nominally for his work on the lighthouse but in reality for his mammoth undertaking. A cairn, in Gaelic and English, celebrating Calum's achievement was erected by the roadside.

The folk-rock band Capercaillie recorded a song entitled 'Calum's Road' in their 1988 album 'The Blood is Strong', a book called *Calum's Road* was published in 2006 and a play about Calum was aired on BBC Radio 4 in 2013. Calum died in Arnish in 1988 but his name lives on as a true local hero.

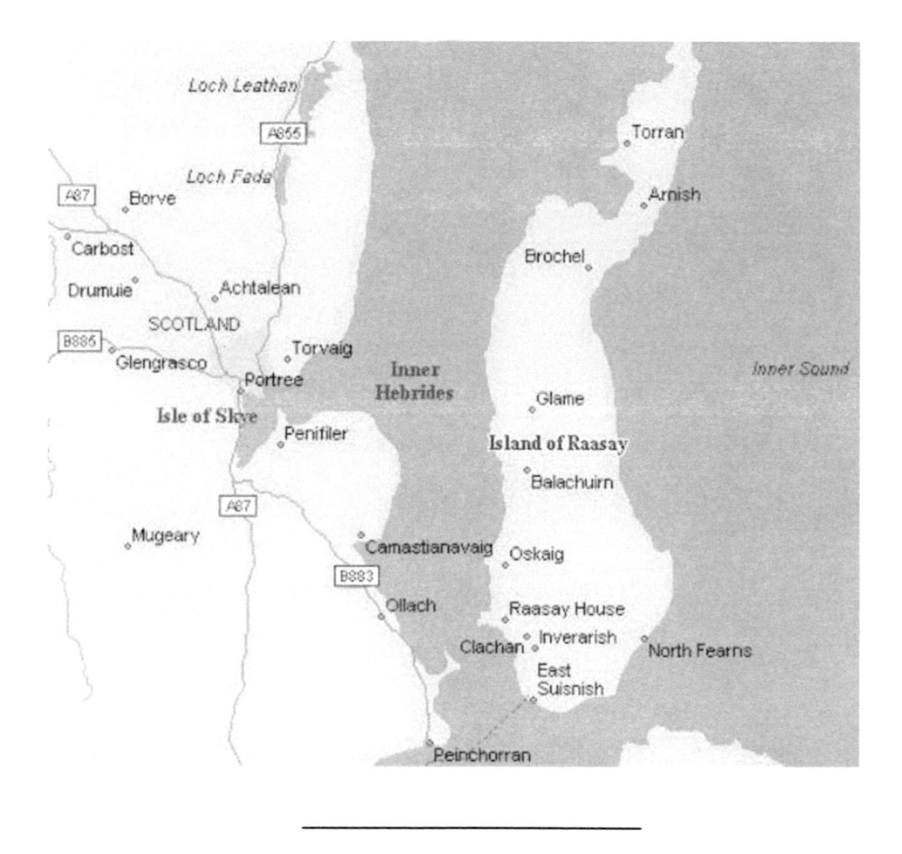

A Highlander carrying a large heavy suitcase got on an old double-decker bus in London. He got into an argument with the conductor, who insisted that he had to pay extra for the suitcase or get off the bus.

The indignant Highlander naturally refused. Exasperated, the conductor threw the suitcase off the bus as they were crossing a bridge over the Thames. The suitcase landed in the river, and it quickly sank. The furious Highlander turned to the conductor and said "Now ye've gone too far! First ye try tae rob me, then ye drown ma wee boy'".

15)

Q: Where is Drumnadrochit?

A:

i) Under your grannie's bed

ii) Borneo

iii) On the western shore of Loch Ness

16)

Q: Which of these statements indicate 'dottled' behaviour?

A:

i) 'Why can't I wear pyjamas in Church Street? ?'

ii) 'Have I ever introduced you to my favourite lamp post?'

iii) 'What did you say my name is?'

15) (Correct: iii)
16) (Correct: all)

Cheuchter Top Ten: 9

Sha-la-la Portree

A perennial coast-wester fave, this cheery, mouth music love ditty is based on the Small Faces 1966 hit 'Sha-la-la-la-lee'. Our particular version is the first-ever Skeenuck rock/pop song, and possibly the first thing they sang in the English language after 'God Save The King'. The raucous, powerful Small Faces original contrasts dramatically with the naturally soft, Gaelic Skye tongue to produce a surprisingly tender, lovelorn ballad, as this first verse and chorus indicate:

First verse

'(A) Picked her up on a (E) snowy night (A)
(D) Sha-la-la Portree (A), aye (E)
(A) She said 'This dance better (E) no' be (A) shite
(D) Sha-la-la (E) Portree (A), aye' (*repeat this line*)

Chorus

'(E) I held her close and asked her if
She would (D) dig ma tatties (A)
(E) It felt so good when she answered me
Piss off, piss off, ye've got yer own spade and shovel, aye...(E7).'

A rebuke, certainly, but one delivered with a typically blunt, practical Skeenuck compassion. If he hadn't got his own spade and shovel, she may well have dug his tatties. Who knows? This air of puzzled conjecture, a cheuchter's natural mindset, is what makes this song so popular all the way from Dunvegan to Uig.

17)

Q: Why was Jesus not born in Nairn?

A:

i) The town did not exist two thousand years ago

ii) Mary and Joseph didn't have enough money for the air fare

iii) They couldn't find three wise men and a virgin

18)

Q: What is a 'cheuchter'?

A:

i) A cute little steam train on the Kyle of Lochalsh railway line

ii) An inhabitant of the northwest Highlands

iii) Someone who can't stop sneezing

19)

Q: What is The Gay Gordons?

A:

i) A secluded allotment where Gordon entertains his closest friends

ii) A Highland army regiment (now amalgamated) who simply adored wearing kilts

iii) A Scottish dance

17) (Correct: iii)

18) (Correct: ii)

19) (Correct: iii)

20)

Q: How does one practise safe sex in Cromarty?

A:

i) Follow the latest NHS guidelines

ii) Make sure that the handbrake is on

iii) Find an empty bus shelter

20) (Correct: ii)

Twenty-five years ago, Alec and Moira were about to get married in Inverness and were talking about where to go for their honeymoon. "Let's just go to Butlins", said Moira. : "No", said Alec. "Let's have an adventure and go to Miami." So, after the wedding at the Old High, they flew to Miami airport, hired a car and drove down Route 1, where they saw a neat roadside sign saying 'Indian Memory Man: turn right'. "Interesting", said Alec, "let's have a look." So they turned right, drove down a clean, well-tended side road, and arrived at a freshly-painted tepee.

They parted the tepee canvas entrance, to find a young Amerindian, with a single feather in his hair. sitting there staring at them. "I am the Indian Memory Man", he said. "Ask me any question and I'll tell you the answer." "All right, I'll bet he doesn't know this one", thought Alec, who said to him "Who won the Inverness Charity Cup Final in 1948 and what was the score?"

The Indian looked at him with piercing eyes and immediately replied "Clach won, beating Caley 4-3". "I don't believe it. He's right", said Alec, who thanked the Memory Man, headed back to the car, and the honeymooners got on with their holiday and soon forgot about their encounter.

To celebrate their Silver Wedding twenty-five years later, they decided to return to Miami. They again hired a car at Miami airport, drove down Route 1, and they saw the same sign, rusty and hanging from one hinge, which said 'Indian Memory Man: turn right'. "Let's see if he's still there", said Moira.

They went down what had become a decrepit side road, shadowed by large pine fronds and covered in weeds, to find a faded old tepee. Through the canvas door they went, and there he was: but this time he had a mane of long silver hair, a full head-dress, and he radiated authority. "He's obviously an important chief now. Treat him with respect", whispered Moira.

"I know how to do it. I've seen it on the telly", said Alec, who strode up to the Amerindian, stood to attention, raised his palm and solemnly intoned "How". The Indian Memory Man lifted his head, gazed at Alec for a moment, and replied "A winning goal in extra time".

21)
Q: Why did Clach not join Caley and Thistle in forming a full Inverness team to compete in the Scottish League in 1994?
A:
i) They couldn't find a coach driver who knew how to get to Glasgow
ii) Their centre half had a groin strain from being thrown out of the Black Bull
iii) No one asked them

22)
Q: What is the significance of the phrase 'Snow on the Ben'?
A:
i) It gives Invernessians something to say to each other on the street: 'There's snow on the Ben'. 'Aye, right 'enuff'
ii) It indicates the arrival of a 90 degree F heatwave, unbroken sunshine and the arrival of the annual surfing season
iii) Winter is on its way

23)
Q: What does the word 'bachle' mean in Inverness?
A:
i) An ancient Celtic word for a 'battle' eg 'The Bachle of Culloden'
ii) An affectionate and loving term of endearment used to greet grannies eg 'Hello grannie, you look more like a bachle every day'
iii) An unkempt, disheveled, bow-legged, untrustworthy old mannie

21) (Correct: i)
22) (Correct: iii)
23) (Correct: iii)

Cheuchter Top Ten: 8

I Can Sing Like Calum Kennedy

The splendid tenor voice and charismatic stage presence of Stornoway-born Highland superstar Calum Kennedy brought him fame and adulation over the last thirty or so years of the 20th century. Although his over-ornate Hielan' dress sense was, to be kind, somewhat eccentric, and often garish, this chart has nothing to do with fashion, so we can forgive him his sartorial excesses. Thousands of cheuchters attempted (rather painfully) to emulate his exceptional singing voice, and a song was even written about him. 'I can sing like Calum Kennedy' is a paen of praise to this man's talent. Here are two of the verses and the chorus (which is in Gaelic, his first language):

a) '(G) I can sing like Calum Kennedy, I can sing like Calum Kennedy
(C) I can sing like (G) Calum Kennedy, (D) that's something I'd like to remedy'

Chorus: '(G) Eechtan eechtan al a'heachin, eechtan eechtan al a'heachin,
(C) Eechtan eechtan (G) al a'heachin, (D) eechtan eechtan, nich nich, noch noch'

b) (*chords as a*): 'Ma grannie looks like Calum Kennedy, ma grannie looks like Calum Kennedy,
Ma grannie looks like Calum Kennedy, that's something she'd like to remedy'

It's a simple song, and can be criticised for its repetitive nature, but it's delightful in its vacant cheeriness. Have you ever had a popular (eighth in the charts) song written about you? Of course you haven't. But you don't possess the late and lamented Calum's coast-wester talent. You may have a similar taste in naff 'kilty danny' leisurewear, but there the resemblance ends. There was only ever one Calum.

24)
Q: What is meant by the word 'pibroch'?
A:
i) A thick mushy soup, for special occasions, made from garden peas
ii) The art of piping and bagpipe playing
iii) Originally the first line of the song 'A pibroch and doris' until Harry Lauder changed it to 'A wee deoch and doris'

25)
Q: Why do otherwise sane people play 'curling'?
A:
i) The bars stay open late at ice rinks and the whisky is cheap
ii) They want to win an Olympic gold medal in a 'sport' played by no other country in the world
iii) It is a fun, sociable and entertaining activity

A old Highlandman set up a stall in a lay-by beside Loch Ness. He had two or three pyramidal heaps of brown balls, about half an inch in diameter, and a big sign saying 'Learning balls: only £10'. Two American tourists, Elmer and Mabel stopped by. Elmer asked the old man what the balls are for. He replied that you eat one and learn something: an old Highland tradition. Elmer, overcome with emotion, handed over £10 and picked a ball. He stuck it in his mouth and began chewing. Seconds later, he spat it out, saying "that tastes like sheep shit". The old man said "aye, ye're learning".

24) (Correct: ii)
25) (Correct: i)

26)

Q: Who or what is the Dashing White Sergeant?

A:

i)) A Nairn policeman who tripped over a tin of white paint while running after his girlfriend

ii) A 'Highland' kiltie dance

iii) Michael Caine in the movie 'Zulu'

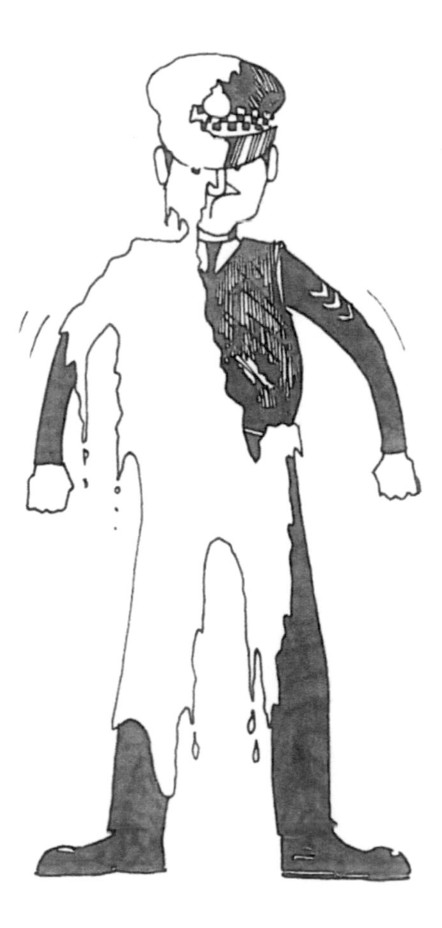

26) (Correct: ii)

Highland Characters: 'Laughing His Head Off'

When the highly regarded website Electric Scotland describes an historical character thus: 'the sole purpose of his life was to promote his own power by all feasible means, this being the only object of his solicitude' and as 'a person too remarkable in history to be overlooked', then one has a compulsion to read on.

The subject of this damning critique is Simon Fraser, the 11th Lord Lovat of the Fraser clan, which came originally from France and was established as the Lords of Lovat in the Beauly area in 1460. The family continues to exist to the present day, and the current title is held by another Simon Fraser.

Clearly the historical black sheep of this noble family, the 11th Lord's life of deception, chicanery and duplicity began in 1667. Notorious for changing his allegiances and for violent feuding, Fraser inherited the title of 11th Lord of Lovat in 1699 and, after a series of outrageous incidents, escaped from a French jail and returned to the Highlands in 1714.

Between the 1715 and 1745 Jacobite Rebellions he switched from being pro-Government to pro-Jacobite. The extent of his scheming machinations was boundless but he managed to retain his Lordship status until shortly after the '45.

Following the Jacobites' disastrous defeat at the Battle of Culloden, and by now an old man, he sat in hiding and watched the government forces raze his home, Dounie Castle, to the ground. Convicted of treason, he was captured on an island in Loch Morar and was sentenced to death after a five-day trial in London.

When he was climbing the scaffold at the Tower of London for his execution, a row of seating set up for spectators collapsed, killing twenty people, an event which greatly amused Fraser. He was still laughing as he was executed. This is said to be the origin of the phrase 'laughing your head off', as it was the last public beheading in Britain. One has to respect the man for facing his grisly death so admirably.

27)

Q: What is the nickname of Inverness Clachnacuddin FC?

A:

I) Lily the Pink

Ii) Lilywhites

Iii) Lill ye no come back again?

28)

Q: Who was the Brahan Seer?

A:

i) The manager of the local optician shop in Brahan

ii) A 17th-century Highlander with the gift of 'second sight'

iii) A Dingwall bookie famous for predicting the wrong shinty results

27) (Correct: ii)
28) (Correct: ii)

29)

Q: What is the meaning of 'quaich'?

A:

i) A circular, twin-handled, Highland drinking vessel

ii) A cheuchter asking for your speedy assistance: 'Be quaich about it'

iii) How you feel when you walk into an alleyway after closing time and find seven brawny, drunk Nairnucks waiting for you

30)

Q: How might one define 'unnatural practices'?

A:

i) Supporting Ross County

ii) Having carnal knowledge of a sheep

iii) Having carnal knowledge of a sheep, a horse and your wife, all at the same time as watching Ross County

31)

Q: What was McDermott's?

A:

i) Anything that belonged to Torquil McDermott

ii) A trendy cocktail bar in the posher suburbs of Cannich

iii) An oilrig fabrication yard near Ardersier

29) (Correct: i)
30) (Correct: i)
31) (Correct: iii)

Cheuchter Top Ten: 7

Clachnaharry On My Mind

Loosely based on the 1971 recording by US singer and songwriter James Taylor, who is now bald and not as pretty as he used to be (but just as compelling a performer). The song contains three verses but, as there is a lot of crying and dark gothic imagery in the lyrics, we don't wish to depress you. So here's the chorus, which is cheerful enough:

'(G) In ma mind I'm (F) goin' to Clachnaharry (D)
(C) Can't you just see the train line (D), (C) can't you just hear Dave Irvine (D)
(E Minor) The bar is grand and so's the wine (C) and the bottles of Ballantine (A7-D)
(G) I'm goin' to (C) Clachnaharry (A7/D) in ma mind (G).'

A friend of mine was so moved by the poignancy of this song that he penned a nostalgic verse about the Gellions Bar between the mid-1960s and the late-1970s. The Gellions, on Inverness's Bridge Street, was home to the town's Folk Club, and was a popular, even trendy, drinking venue for the local youthful 'glitterati'. Coincidentally, there is a connection between the Clachnaharry Bar and the Gellions, as the Dave Irvine mentioned in the above song used to own and run the Gellions. My friend describes his memories thus (using the same chord structure and tune as 'Clachnaharry'):

'In my mind I'm sitting in the Gellions
Drinking pints of Heavy
It's my favourite bevvy
And Mrs Ross or Chrissie tops me up from time to time
I'm sitting in the Gellions in my mind'

The James Taylor album also includes other classics, which we have borrowed, such as the romantic Highland lullaby 'Sweet Baby Jimmuck' ('Goodnight, you Merkinch wifies / Rockabye Sweet Baby Jimmuck...) and 'Fired Once Again' ('I've been fired once again / I've seen sunny days disappearing from the Ben / But I've got a new job up in Craig Dunain / Where I'm bound to get myself fired yet again'. Great days, indeed, and fine music.

---

32)
Q: Who or what were the 'Picts'?
A:
i) A visit to an Inverness cinema: 'I'm off to the Picts the night'
ii) An ancient, pre-Gaelic tribe who ran most of Scotland
iii) Sharp tools used in rock quarries, along with spades and shovels

A guy walks up to the turnstile at the Clach Park to watch a game. He takes out a £50 note and says to the lady at the turnstyle 'I'm sorry, but this is all I've got. Is it too much?'

The lady replies 'Well, it depends whether you want a forward or a defender'.

32) (Correct: ii)

33)
Q: Where or what is Dores?
A:
i) A hamlet on the northeast shore of Loch Ness
ii) An annual Inverness event where everyone called Jim ('Jeemuck') Morrison gathers to sing 'Light my Fire'
iii) Entrances in houses: 'will ye shut these Dores, ye wee bugger?'

34)
Q: Who was King Brude?
A:
i) Lead singer with King Brude and the Brudders and occasional vocal partner of Dingwall rock star Craig Dunain in the early 1960s
ii) A racehorse from Balnafettack that finished last in the 1723 Haugh Grand National
iii) Ruler of the Pictish nation in the 6th century AD

33) (Correct: i)
34) (Correct: iii)

35)

Q: What are the Falls of Foyers?

A:

i) The steps leading down from the Foyers Hotel public bar on a Friday night

ii) A nickname for the MacPhauls, a notorious family of sheep-shaggers who once lived in the Foyers area

iii) A magnificent waterfall which plunges from Foyers into Loch Ness

36)

Q: What is the Camanachd Cup?

A:

i) The bra size of a big lassie from Beauly

ii) A prestigious shinty trophy

iii) A china tea cup which Stornoway grannies give to the meenister

35) (Correct: iii)
36) (Correct: ii)

Two English guys working in Easter Ross were staggering back to their digs from the local pub one night, when they came across a couple of locals. One was dangling the other over a bridge by his feet. Suddenly, the dangling local started shouting “Quick... pull me up now Rab”. Rab pulled him up, and his friend landed on the bridge holding a ten-pound salmon. The two Englishmen decided that this was a great idea, and took off to find another bridge. When they found a bridge, one of them went over the side, and immediately started screaming “PULL ME UP... PULL ME UP”. When his mate asked "Where’s the fish?" he replied 'Fish? What fish? There’s a train coming!"

An American rancher met up with a local farmer at the Black Isle Show. The rancher asked the farmer how much land he had, and the farmer replied "about 150 acres". The American said "well, it can take me two days just to drive round my ranch". The farmer said "aye, I used to have a car like that".

Jimmy McTavish was lying on his death bed in his Inverness home. His wife Isla whispered softly to him "can ah get ye somethin', Jeemuck? It could be yer last ever request." Jimmy slowly raised his head and plaintively whispered "a wee bit o' boiled ham wid be nice". Isla stared at him. "Ye can't have that, Jemuck", she replied. "Ah'm keepin' the ham for the funeral."

The act of 'sheep shagging', or carnal knowledge of a creature of the ovine persuasion, is rare in the Highlands, and the epithet 'sheep shagger' is normally employed as an insult and not as an accurate description of one's antagonist's sexual proclivities.

However, as Mick Jagger reportedly discovered, this unnatural obscenity is not completely unknown. The pouty-lipped songster was about to buy a farm near Drumnadrochit, and he asked a local character, named MacLeod, to investigate the quality, physical and moral, of the local farm animals. Jagger was shocked the following morning to observe his new employee in a compromising position with a sheep, and exclaimed "Hey, MacLeod, get offa ma ewe".

He swiftly abandoned his plans to be a Highland country gentleman and flew back to London. However, the lyric for a song was germinating in his mind...

37)

Q: What was the attraction of 'Hunters'' in Inverness High Street?

A:

i) A space where kids could play 'Cowboys and Indians'

ii) Billiard tables

iii) They sold posh, expensive wellies

38)

Q: What today is a Jacobite?

A:

i) A tartan-wrapped cream cracker

ii) A Wee Free sect which follows the Biblical teachings of Jacob, grandson of Abraham

iii) A company which runs cruise boats up and down Loch Ness

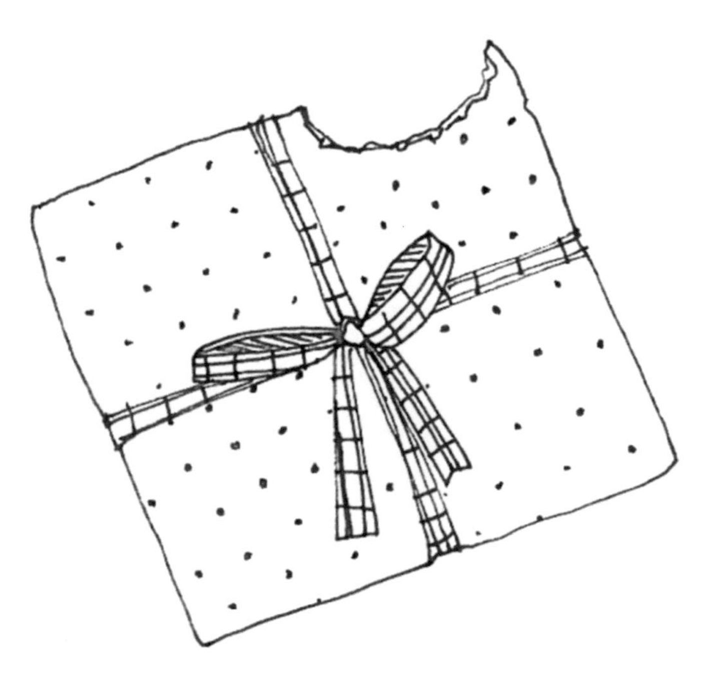

37) (Correct: ii)

38) (Correct: iii)

39)

Q: With which fruit or vegetable does one associate Balnafettack?

A:

i) Sun-dried mangoes

ii) Tatties

iii) Opium poppies

40)

Q: Who in Inverness was 'Mackles'?

A:

i) Owner of a large shooting estate near Kessock Ferry and one-time Conservative Party candidate for the Inverness area

ii) Alex Mapplebeck, a Merkinch 'character' and penalty-taking coach for Clach

iii) Principal counter-tenor and harpsichordist with the Grant Street Operatic Society

39) (Correct: ii)

40) (Correct: ii)

Highland Characters: 'Gentle' Lochiel

One does not have to believe in the cause of the Stuart dynasty or the validity of the 1745 Jacobite Rebellion, which was doomed from the outset, in order to appreciate the courage and gallantry of Donald Cameron of Lochiel, the 19th hereditary Chief of the Clan Cameron.

After the failure of the 1715 Jacobite Rebellion, the government enacted the Statutes of Iona which ordered all clan chiefs and their heirs to be relocated and educated in the Scottish Lowlands at English-speaking, Protestant schools, in what was an obvious attempt to suppress the Gaelic language and culture. Donald then had to live in Edinburgh and, in common with the other chiefs, spent much of the clan's money on maintaining a comfortable lifestyle, thereby impoverishing his clansmen.

However, he remained a supporter of the Stuart cause. In the early 1740s the Hanoverian government discovered that Donald had been communicating with Charles Edward Stuart and issued a warrant for his arrest for treason. When Charles Stuart arrived in Scotland in August 1745, with little of the support which the French had promised, many of the leading clans were not interested in another uprising and did not support the 'Young Pretender'.

Although Donald was also initially reluctant, he was eventually persuaded by Charles to join him, and the Clan Cameron became Charles' supporters. Donald had little knowledge of military affairs but he was a brave, selfless commander. The Jacobites defeated the Hanoverian forces at Prestonpans and occupied Edinburgh. His generous, forgiving nature was demonstrated when he ordered no reprisals against the Hanoverian Whigs, and he also ensured that all injured enemy soldiers were cared for after Prestonpans.

He tried to persuade Charles not to move south, and after their retreat north from Derby Donald was wounded at the Battle of Falkirk in January 1746. Three months later he fought at Culloden, where he personally charged the Hanoverian lines but he was carried wounded from the field. He eventually escaped to France in October 1746, and died there two years later.

Donald Cameron's loyalty, decency and gracious nature earned him respect and the enduring soubriquet of 'Gentle' Lochiel'.

41)
Q: What is the 'Nairn straight'?
A:
i) Corruption of 'strait', ie crossing the Firth from Nairn to Black Isle
ii) An eight-mile section of straight road betwen Inverness and Nairn
iii) The only heterosexual still resident in Nairn

42)
Q: What is the origin of the word 'Lovat'?
A:
i) A beautiful glen, near Muir of Ord, adored by visitors
ii) Low value-added-tax (found only in medieval Beauly)
iii) A rotten, smelly, putrefying area of bogland

41) (Correct: ii)
42) (Correct: iii)

Cheuchter Top Ten: 6

Space Bodach

A Hielan' tribute to David Bowie's futuristic late-1960s song 'Space Oddity'. 'Space Bodach' is also a reminder of the perils of the over-ambitious Easter Ross Space Programme, poignantly expressed here in the concluding lines when our astronaut hero discovers his situation is hopeless:

Message from an increasingly desperate Ground Control (Phoenix Bar):
'(G) Phoenix Bar to Willie John
(A Minor) It's closing time, yer (A Minor7) wife's jist gone
Wi' a (D7) cheuchter from Kishorn (repeat this line)
Can ye (G) hear me Willie John, can you...'

Response from bodach:
'(F Major7) ... here am I floatin' over Cannich (E Minor)
(F Major7) Dingwall's comin' soon (E Minor)
(B Flat Major7) I'll be landing in Bunchrew (A Minor7)
And there's nuthin' (G) I can do (F)...

Instrumental interval / conclusion: C-C / F-F-G / A-A (ad infinitum, if required)

There is little remaining to say about this tragic tale, other than that the Easter Ross Space Programme has been wound down and our bodach is probably still circling the galaxies, crying 'I want my mither or ma grannie'. This is a heartbreakingly splendid song.

In the 1970s, two American tourists, with cameras round necks, baseball hats, 'I Love Nessie' T-shirts and well-thumbed copies of *'Malt Whiskies Of The World: A Connoisseur's Guide'* walked into the bar of the old Cummings Hotel (alas, now departed) on Church Street.

They asked the barman for a couple of the bar's finest malts. The barman, a smart bow-tied gentleman who possessed a fond and deep knowledge of malt whisky, was delighted to explain patiently and at length the virtues of the leading Highlands' distilleries and their top-of-the-range malt products. The Yanks finally made their choices. They then asked for these excellent malts to be topped up with lemonade.

'Certainly, gentlemen', replied the deadpan barman. 'Would you prefer Hays or Bon Accord?'

(This true story was told to us by Clive Windsor, Clach goalie in the 1970s, who happened to be there)

Hamish was sitting alongside a smug teetotalier on an air flight, starting at Dalcross, to the United States. The stewardess came past: "can I get you something, gentlemen?" "Aye, I'll have a big whisky", said Hamish. The other guy answered "I'd rather be ravished by a beautiful woman all the way to the USA than drink that stuff".

Hamish looked at the stewardess, handed back the whisky, and said to her "ye never told me there was a choice".

43)
Q: Who wrote the poem 'The Lovely Lass Of Inverness'?
A:
i) Ivor Cutler
ii) Rabbie Burns
iii) Alan Ginsberg

44)
Q: What or where is 'Grannie's Hielan' Hame'
A:
i) An embarrassingly maudlin song written in the 1920s
ii) A holiday park in Embo near Dornoch
iii) Wherever she wants it to be

43) (Correct: ii)
44) (Correct: ii)

Cheuchter Top Ten: 5

Greig Street Bridge Song

This romantic traditional ballad is a nostalgic stumble over a much-loved Inverness landmark, which is an escape route over the River Ness from the stultifyingly boring bourgeois Crown area to the magnificent Clach Park and the hidden hedonistic pleasures of Dalneigh and the Merkinch. The amount of time spent on crossing this shaky Victorian pedestrian bridge is a function of on how long one has spent that particular evening in the Phoenix Bar (ie the more pints you've had, the longer it takes to cross), so the number of verses varies accordingly. The version containing the most verses is to be found in the Friday night rendition of the song as, understandably, this is when the bridge can take quite a while to navigate (or even find). The first verse begins:

'(C) I love to go a-wanderin' across the Greig Street Bridge (G) When skippin' there beside (C) me are old Mackles (F) and (G) Dan Fridge (C)'.

The chorus starts: 'Fol-de re (G),' and ends '(G) wi' ma carry-oot on ma back (C)'. It must be said that it's a rather boring chorus with far too much unfunny, tedious, phoney laughter and manufactured joie de vivre, particularly when it is sung by Kenneth MacKellar or Andy Stewart, although Calum makes a noble attempt at it, but the verse lyrics are splendid, as is the tune. The song is a deserved tribute to a splendid old walkway.

45)

Q: Why is there not a Zoo in Inverness?

A:

i) There is no letter 'z' in Gaelic, and you can't really call it an 'oo'

ii) 'Zoo' isn't mentioned in the Bible, so the Wee Frees won't allow it

iii) No one can be bothered building one

46)

Q: What is the point of Inverness Castle?

A:

i) It's a proud symbol of Inverness's Royal Burgh status

ii) It's a handy place to hide away with schoolmates and drink cider

iii) It's the ugliest, most inappropriate 'castle' in the world, and therefore of great interest to architects

47)

Q: What was the main dialect in Caithness until the 17th century?

A:

i) Gaelic

ii) Norn

iii) Hungarian

45) (Correct: iii)
46) (Correct: ii)
47) (Correct: ii)

48)

Q: What is the original Gaelic meaning of 'sassenach'?

A:

i) An Englishman (derived fom 'Saxon')

ii) A Pictish saxophone used in Druidic rituals

iii) A Lowland Scot

48) (Correct: iii)

49)

Q: The Battle of Mons Graupius was fought in 84 AD between the Romans and the Picts. Who was the Pictish leader?

A:

i) Caligula

ii) Calum Kennedy

iii) Calcagus

50)

Q: What was the result of this battle?

A:

i) The Romans claimed victory

ii) The Picts decided to go home

iii) No one is very sure

49) (Correct: iii)

50) (Correct: iii)

51)

Q: What activity is most closely associated with Belladrum?

A:

i) A prestigious Italian percussion academy

ii) An annual contemporary music festival

iii) A rehearsal centre for Drumnadrochit campanologists

52)

Q: What do Highlanders call the plant known in England as Sweet William?

A:

i) Common tansy ragwort

ii) A delightfully ornamental addition to one's garden environment

iii) 'Stinking Willy' (in honour of Prince William, Duke of Cumberland)

51) (Correct: ii)

52) (Correct: iii)

Highland Characters: Highland 'man o' pairts'

The small, pretty Highland town of Cromarty in Easter Ross might seem an unlikely place to have given birth to one of the great 19th-century natural scientists of his age. However, Hugh Miller, who was born there in 1802, certainly qualifies for such a title. Indeed, one could go further and describe Miller as a polymathic genius, who was a geologist, writer, folklorist, historian and leading Christian evangelist.

His apprenticeship to a local stonemason when he was 17 years old, and his investigations of the local quarries and the Cromarty Firth shoreline, led to his lifelong, self-taught interest in geology. He wrote several highly influential books on the subject (particularly on Old Red Sandstone), although his evangelistic beliefs persuaded him to accept much of Genesis as the literal truth but he did believe in the great age of the Earth.

He also wrote poetry, non-scientific essays and a history of Cromarty. In the 1840s he was influential in the 'Disruption' of the Church of Scotland and was a leading member of the 'Wee Frees', in which capacity he was editor of the breakaway group's newspaper, 'The Witness'.

He was what may today be described as a 'psychotic depressive', and this tall, imposing man shot himself in 1856 in Edinburgh and died of his injuries. Today, he is considered to have been one of Scotland's leading palaeontologists, and his bust is in the Wallace Monument in Stirling.

The Cromarty cottage, built in 1698, in which he was born - 'Hugh Miller's Cottage' - remains a tribute to the man. It contains a museum which displays many of his geological artefacts, and also a beautiful small garden. Without doubt, Miller was one of the great men of the 19th century, and it is a pity that his work is not generally as well-known and respected as it deserves to be.

53)
Q: Why is Cape Wrath, the most northwesterly point in Britain, so called?
A:
i) It acts as a stern reminder of God's anger
ii) It is used by the MoD as a firing range
iii) It is a corruption of the Old Norse 'hvarf' meaning 'turning point'

54)
Q: What area has been described as 'The Brighton of Scotland'?
A:
i) The Merkinch
ii) Nairn
iii) The Longman

55)
Q: Which is the oldest Royal Burgh in Scotland?
A:
i) Abriachan
ii) Tain
iii) Clachnaharry

53) (Correct: iii)
54) (Correct: ii)
55) (Correct: ii)

56)

Q: How many forenames had Bonny Prince Charlie?

i) One

ii) Two

iii) Eight

57)

Q: What is 'El Kessocko'?

A:

i) A charming little tapas bar just south of Rosemarkie

ii) A Spanish-language guide to Grant Street's attractions

iii) A regular football match between Ross County and Caley Thistle

56) (Correct: iii)

57) (Correct: iii)

Cheuchter Top Ten: 4

Shinin' Heather

This song is included herein with some trepidation, but the fact that it is frequently requested by English incomers on Highland radio shows insists on its elevated position in this listing. To the tune of 'Scotland the Brave', here are a couple of verses and the chorus:

'(D) Land o' the shinin' heather
Land o' the whinin' blether
(G) Land o' the (D) never-never
(A) Scotland the grave (A7)'

Chorus: (A) Cowerin' in pouring rain
I'm (D) in Scotland yet again
'(D) Blimey, but it's (G) cold here', says my (A) English mate Dave (A7)'

'(D) High in the freezin' Highlands
Stuck on the snowy Islands
(G) Why do these (D) midgies eat me?
(A) Bloody Scottish flies (A7)'

Insulting to Scotland, yes, but the lyrics to the original 'Scotland the Brave' are not as ancient as you may suppose. The original song was written by Glasgow journalist Cliff Hanley in the 1950s, and was adopted by the Scottish international football team as their anthem in the 1982 and 1986 World Cup finals, which could explain their shambolic performances in these tournaments. And I suppose that anything is better than 'Flower of Scotland'.

However, the lyrics appear to refer more to the sassenach Scottish Lowlands than to our cheuchter lands of the north. The song possibly arose as a reaction to the football chant 'If ye hate the English, clap yer hands'. We Highlanders are of a more tolerant, forgiving nature than the afore-mentioned tribes, but the English are getting their own back in 'Shinin' Heather'.

This fact may astonish some of this volume's younger readers (those aged under fifty), but there was a time when the now ubiquitous and extravagant bar lunches, served today virtually everywhere in Inverness, were rarely offered in the town's public houses. They were perceived as something of an unnecessary luxury, a middle-class frippery.

Indeed, one day in the late 1960s an irate and flustered American woman stormed into the Gellions and berated the barman (who was called Henry and who is fondly remembered for his rejoinders to some of the daft questions he was continually being asked): 'I've been to several bars and they are hopeless. Where can I get lunch in this goddam town?'

Henry put down the glass he was washing, looked at her and replied 'I'm afraid I don't know, lady. I go home for mine.'

(This is a true story, as I was sitting at the bar at the time)

Young Hamish was nursing a pint of McEwan's Export in the old Harbour Inn in Nairn when his pal Jimmuck walked in. 'You look gey pleased wi' yersel', said Jimmuck. 'Aye', replied a smug Hamish, 'I'm gettin' married next week.' ' Congratulation. Who's the lucky lassie?' asked Jimmuck. 'Jessie Miller from Auldearn', said Hamish proudly.

'Jessie Miller! Hamish, half the guys in Auldearn have had her', said Jimmuck. 'Aye, but it's no a very big place', replied Hamish.

58)
Q: How deep is Loch Ness?
A:
i) 800 feet
ii) Think of the Maracaibo Trench, then add a bit
iii) Two feet six inches

59)
Q: What in the Inverness area is known as 'the hill of the fairies'?
A:
i) The Crown area
ii) Tomnahurich Cemetery
iii) Porterfield Prison

60)
Q: What is Inverness City?
A:
i) The Highland Dingwall
ii) A football team in the Junior SuperLeague
iii) A better name than Inverness Caledonian Thistle

58) (Correct: i)
59) (Correct: ii)
60) (Correct:ii and iii)

61)

Q: Where is the General's Well?

A:

i) The Cameron Barracks

ii) The Ness Islands

iii) Fort George

62)

Q: What is a 'haugh'?

A:

i) A smoked ham joint used to make soup

ii) The sound a heavy smoker makes when clearing his throat

iii) A flat piece of land by a river (in Inverness, The Haugh runs along the south side of the river below the Castle)

61) (Correct: ii)

62) (Correct: ii and iii)

63)

Q: Who or what are 'the Godsies'?

A:

i) Another nickname for 'wee frees'

ii) A steep path from the Haugh to Culduthel Road

iii) A teenage gang of Crown area mutants descended from Godzilla

64)

Q: Who or what was La Scala?

A:

i) Giovanni Claudio La Scala, a Clach inside-left sent off against Caley in 1926 for singing an operatic aria

ii) A windswept uninhabited island in Orkney, famous for its orange groves

iii) A dingy old Inverness picture house

63) (Correct: ii)

64) (Correct: iii)

Cheuchter Top Ten: 3

In Strathpeffer

Another local gem, with its melodic origin being John Martyn's 'May You Never' from his 1974 album 'Solid Air', a product of his Abriachan creative period. He has, alas, subsequently limped off the planet to entertain that Great Cheuchter in the Sky. Here are the opening and closing lines of this most moving of songs, which refers to the weekly dance at the Strath Pavilion:

a) '(G/G7) In Strath (C) peffer keep your (A Minor) head down
(G) Unless you're feeling (C) bold
In Strathpeffer you're in (G) trouble if you're (C) old'

Middle section '(G) You're just like a (C) big strong (D) brother to me (G)
(G) You're just like a (D) Wee Free too
(G)There's a cheuchter from (C) Beauly with a (D) knife at my back (G)
(G) And I hope that you'll (D) help me through (G)
(D) Please won't you take the knife away from him
(C) Or I'll never go (D) dancing again with you, no (G)
(D) Please won't you, please won't you stop coming
(C) To the (D) Pavilion no more (G)'

b) (same chords as a) 'In Strathpeffer it's too easy
To get in a bar-room fight
If not, there'll be one on the bus home on Friday night'

Despite John Martyn being generally known for soft jazzy folk guitar, he was never averse to the odd punch-up, and this version of his song reveals both sides to his nature. The weekly 1960s Strathpeffer Pavilion Dance was notorious for the fights which occurred there as much as for the celebrity bands it managed to stage. These days, dancers conduct themselves in a more conventional and polite but dull manner.

Highland Characters: How To Be Both

The Highlands of Scotland has given birth to, nurtured and been a welcoming home to numerous internationally-praised novelists, poets, literary critics, essayists and writers of all descriptions.

The Highland Capital of Inverness (not formally a 'capital' of anything but by some distance the largest conurbation in the region) has long played its part in fostering the Highlands' creative talent: musical, artistic and literary. Today, the city can lay claim to being the birthplace of one of the finest and internationally most acclaimed novelists and short story writers in the world of contemporary literature.

Ali Smith was born in 1962 in a council house in the Dalneigh area of the town and attended Inverness High School. Her older sister, Anne, now McLeod, was a classmate of mine in the old Inverness Royal Academy. In 2015 Ali won the prestigious Baileys Womens Prize for Fiction for her novel *How To Be Both*. The book, which juxtaposes the lives of a contemporary teenage girl and a Renaissance artist, was described by the judges as 'tender, brilliant and witty' and her work was compared to James Joyce and Virginia Woolf.

Ali, who now lives in Cambridge, has written four short story collections and seven novels, three of which were shortlisted for the Man Booker award, and she has now achieved the recognition which her work has long deserved.

Ali's first collection of short stories, *Free Love*, was published in 1995 and it received several Scottish literary awards. Since then, she has immersed herself in the world of literature as a full-time author, literary critic and book festival host and guest speaker, and her appearances at literary events are well attended, often controversial but always much appreciated by her audiences. In

2007 she was appointed a Fellow of the Royal Society of Literature, and in 2015 she was awarded a CBE for services to literature.

She is currently at work on another novel and, still only in her mid-50s, this prolific and hugely talented Invernessian author appears to have a glittering and increasingly rewarding future awaiting her.

Premier League football club Ross County were determined to win the League for the first time in their history. They decided that the best way to achieve this was to notify clubs around the world that they were interested in buying a new striker, whose goals would win them the trophy.

The club soon hear from a club in Iraq about a supposedly brilliant 17-year-old striker on their books. The manager flies to Iraq, watches the kid play, and discovers that he is indeed a special player. So the club buys him and flies him over to Dingwall, Ross County's home town.

A month later, Ross County are playing Celtic, who are equal on points, in the last game of the season, and County are 4-0 down with only 20 minutes remaining. In a desperate gamble, the County manager decides to move the young Iraqi off the substitutes' bench onto the pitch. The lad is a sensation, scores five goals, and Ross County win the Premier League.

The fans and local media are overwhelmed by this young genius, but eventually he shakes off all the attention and phones his Mum to tell her about the game. 'Hello, Mum', he says, excitedly, 'I've just scored five goals in twenty minutes, we won the Premier League, and everyone here loves me'.

'Wonderful', says Mum. 'While you were having such a great time, your father was shot in the street, your sister and I were badly beaten up, and your brother has joined a gang of vicious muggers.'

'Mum, I'm really sorry', said the upset kid. 'Sorry!', his Mum exclaims. 'You should be. It's your fault we all moved to Dingwall in the first place!'

65)

Q: To what does the word 'blooter' refer?

A:

i) An early period in Picasso's development (his 'Blooter Period')

ii) A confused state brought about by excess alcohol consumption

iii) A shorthand name, used by naturalists, to describe a Blue Terrapin ('Blue-Ter'), common in the Highlands

65) (Correct: ii)

66)

Q: Where did the Duke of Cumberland keep his armies the night before Culloden?

A:

i) Near Nairn

ii) Near Edinburgh

iii) Up his sleevies

67)

Q: What is the commonly accepted origin of the placename 'Beauly'?

A:

i) From the Gaelic 'beul ath': 'mouth of the ford'

ii) From the 13th-15th century Valliscaulian monks' 'prioritus de belle loco': 'priory of the lovely spot'

iii) From Mary Queen of Scots 'beau lieu': 'beautiful place'

68)

Q: Which was Inverness's first football club?

A:

i) Clach

ii) The Craig Phadraig Picties

iii) Inverness Citadel

66) (Correct: i)

67) (Correct: iii)

68) (Correct: iii)

69)
Q: How many virgins came down from Inverness?
A:
i) One, who wasn't a virgin any more by the time she'd arrived at Waverley Station
ii) 'How many what? Ye're kiddin''
iii) Four and twenty

70)
Q: Why 'four and twenty' virgins?
A:
i) They only asked people in Kenneth Street
ii) The twenty-fifth virgin was on holiday in Tain
iii) It has a poetic lilt to it (unlike the rest of the 'poem')

69) (Correct: iii)
70) (Correct: iii)

Cigarbox Don Sings Country

The two songs on these two pages are by Oban 's very own Donald Jacks, aka 'Cigarbox Don'. He was discovered by a Kessock Books colleague in a cafe above a charity shop in Dingwall, playing cigar box guitar accompanied by his musical buddy on tea chest bass.

The songs were written in affectionate homage to the Kings of Country, Kenny Rogers and Jim Reeves. The first, 'The Mumbler' is sung to the tune of 'The Gambler', and the second, 'The Highland Dating Song', to the melody of 'He'll have to go' by the incomparable Jim Reeves (of the 'what sings and flies into mountains?' joke). You can see and listen to the originals on the hyperlink addresses after each song.

Unfortunately, they were offered to us too late to be included in the Cheuchter Top Ten listings but, by the next edition of this book, who knows? Cigarbox is a rare talent.

The Mumbler

On a dark dreary evening on a bus out of Dingwall
I met up with this gadgie, we were both to drunk to talk
He handed me his carry out, spring roll and soggy noodles
And a stir fry from Cookies that had never seen a wok.

We both sat there staring at the raindrops on the window
Then he turned around and looked me up and down
He said, Son, I'm a promoter, a toker and Yes voter
And tonight I got this awesome gig in town.

I took my cigarbox from my fake plastic gig bag
Told him I can play the blues
He said, Young man, your booked and that's how I got hooked
So come along and join the craic you've nothing left to lose.

Turned out he had a tea chest, a string and a broom handle
I would sing and he would pluck away
And so us old fellas became Slim Panatellas
And the bad news is that we're here to stay.

You gotta know when to pluck em, know when to chuck em
Know when to walk away, know when to fake.
We never count our takings, that's a joke still in the making
So give us some polite applause. Oh please, for goodness sake.

https://www.youtube.com/watch?v=Jj4nJ1YEAp4

The Highland Dating Song

So put your sweet lips a little closer to your mobile
Your profile tells me that you're young and nubile
Your avatar looks so inviting on the screen
Ah! Just wait until you meet this old has-been.

I have studied all your pastimes and your likes
You're into cats and country walks and riding bikes
You want a guy who has own teeth and hair
Just a pity i don't have mine any mair

You can write anything you like on this cyber dating site
Have you lied about your age, oh yes, I thought you might,
I can hear it in your voice you're no spring chick
I think it's just as well you live in Wick.

https://www.youtube.com/watch?v=nlsOzrxx7UY

71)
Q: What was the Lochiel?
A:
i) A clan chief from Lochaber
ii) A famed Grant Street bar, with a sign saying 'please do not ask for credit as a belt in the mouth may offend'
iii) A 'Highland country dance' performed by upper-class worthies at the Inverness Northern Meeting Ball

72)
Q: What is an 'Outlander'?
A:
i) A car of Japanese origin
ii) A foreigner or newcomer to the Highlands
iii) A timetravelling, bodice-ripping book and TV series based around Inverness

73)
Q: What is the Great Glen?
A:
i) The Highland branch of the Glen Campbell Fan Club, based in Culbokie (theme tune: 'By the time I get to Fortrose...')
ii) A magnificent waterway stretching from Fort William to Inverness
iii) A magician with a weekly residence at Grannie's Heilan' Hame

71) (Correct: i or ii)
72) (Correct: all three)
73) (Correct: ii)

74)

Q: How does one address an Inverness police officer?

A:

i) 'Good afternoon, officer'

ii) 'Och, it'll no' happen again, Hamish'

iii) 'Sorry about yer jacket, Wullie, I'll ha'e it cleaned'

75)

Q: Which internationally famous star of the black and white movies era regularly holidayed in Nairn?

A:

i) Fatty Arbuckle

ii) Charlie Chaplin

iii) Clara Bow

(74) (Correct: all and many more)

(75) (Correct: ii)

'Black Gold, Texas Tea ...'

These words are from the theme song to the old TV series 'The Beverley Hillbillies', and they are as apt a description as any to describe the unprecedented impact the North Sea Oil discoveries of the late 1960s had on the Highlands.

The BP rig Sea Gem struck gas in the West Sole Field in September 1965. This was the first North Sea discovery and many more were to follow, including the giant Forties in 1970 and Brent in 1971. Global factors, including OPEC policies, were pushing oil and gas prices increasingly higher in the early 1970s and these, coupled with UK domestic issues, combined to make North Sea fossil fuels highly attractive and profitable commodities. Oil companies needed platforms built at almost any price, and the result was a flurry of activity throughout the UK to get on the fabrication bandwagon.

In the Highlands, the Brown and Root/Wimpey consortium identified a site at Nigg in Easter Ross, and in 1972 they set about creating a vast graving, or 'dry', dock with what is still today the largest moveable dock gate in Europe. In this dock, and fed by the surrounding fabrication shops and support services, they built the early giant BP platforms and remained active for most of the next 25 years. Meanwhile, at Ardersier, the Louisiana-based J Ray McDermott Inc. created a sheltered harbour stretching over a kilometre, fronting an 800-acre site and including an eight-acre fabrication shed into which Hampden Park could easily have fitted.

The core workforce in each yard remained steady, at around 1200-1500, for many years, supplemented by travelling workers in peak times. For some time they were among the highest-paid industrial workers in the UK. However, by the 1990s, market conditions had become very challenging, and the two yards joined forces in 1995 to trade as Barmac. This was partially successful until the early 2000s when both yards closed.

Nigg was taken over by Global Energy Group in 2010 and, following serious investment by them, new life has been breathed into the yard and harbour, providing much-needed jobs, training and business opportunities.

Ardersier, meanwhile, has been connected with marina and housing developments and, more recently, renewables work, but it remains a ghostly reminder of the past. It has been suggested that a permanent memorial would be appropriate to remind people of the huge economic contribution which the Ardersier yard made to the local economy as well as to remember the lives lost in the process.

The Kishorn yard was created slightly later, in the mid 1970s and, although shorter-lived than Nigg or Ardersier, also made a significant contribution to the industry. The Ninian Central concrete platform when floated out from Kishorn was, at that time, the heaviest object ever moved by man across the face of the world. Kishorn closed as a working yard many years ago but, as its facilities are still in place, this yard may yet rise again to work in renewables or decommissioning.

The combination of circumstances which created the yards in the 1970s will probably never be repeated, but we should remember, and be grateful for, the enormous boost it delivered to the Highland economy, the effects of which are still being enjoyed today. And it was fun while it lasted.

Cheuchter Top Ten: 2

No Sheep Blues

A somewhat obscure but unsurpringly popular song with our listener(s), particularly a couple of farmers from Kiltarlity. 'No Sleep Blues' is the second track on the Incredible String Band's '5000 Spirits' 1967 album, and is the inspiration for this sad lament of the eternal triangle between a lovesick coo, a cheuchter and his ovine companion. There is not enough space here to print all the verses, but here is the chorus:

'(*D/E Minor*) The ewe comes sneakin' up
When it thinks ah'm no' lookin' (*E Minor, 7th fret*)
Ah'm startin' to (*G7*) grieve, mun
I used to love the coo before the sheep, mun
They told me sheep are a gas
And they fit in the wellies
But ah'm (*C*) sorry for the coo
And ah've (*G7*) really got the no sheep blues (*C*).'

Highland Lonely Hearts

We recently stumbled across a number of genuine personal ads which have appeared in various newspapers. We have selected a few in order to demonstrate the self-abasement, perversity and sheer desperation of some people who are in need of companionship. We would acknowledge the source of this unusual collecting hobby if only we knew his or her identity. Anyway, here is a small sample of the entries from these wretched souls.

Bitter, disillusioned guy from Beauly, lately rejected by longtime fiancée, seeks decent, honest, reliable woman, if such a thing still exists in this cruel world of hatchet-faced bitches.

Artistic Daviot woman, 44, petite, loves rainy walks on the beach, writing poetry, unusual sea-shells and interesting brown rice dishes, seeks mystic dreamer for companionship, back rubs and more as we bounce along like little tumbling clouds on life's beautiful crazy journey. Strong stomach essential.

Chartered accountant, 54, Dores area, seeks female for marriage. Duties will include cooking, light cleaning and accompanying me to office social functions. References required. No timewasters.

Bad-tempered, foul-mouthed old bastard living in a damp cottage in the arse end of Muir of Ord seeks attractive 21-year old blonde lady with big chest.

Devil-worshipper, Dingwall area, seeks like-minded lady for wining and dining, good conversation, dancing, romantic walks and slaughtering dogs in cemeteries at midnight under the flinty light of a pale moon.

Inverness man, 27, medium build, brown hair, blue eyes, seeks alibi for the night of February 27 between 8pm and 11.30pm.

Recognise yourself?

76)
Q: What was a 'mormaer'?
A:
i) The beseeching call of a Glaswegian beggar
ii) A member of the Church of Latter-Day Saints
iii) A senior Pictish adminstrator

77)
Q: Which of these music legends performed at the Inverness Folk Festival in the 1960s?
A:
i) Martin Carthy
ii) Davy Graham
iii) Bert Jansch

76) (Correct: iii)
77) (Correct: all... and John Martyn, Jeannie Robertson, Hamish Imlach, Archie Fisher, Billy Connolly, Hamish Henderson...)

78)
Q: What are the 'Raining Stairs'?
A:
i) A steep, stepped brae from Castle Street to the Crown
ii) A track from Led Zeppelin's first album
iii) A Highland term for a rainstorm (not an uncommon event)

79)
Q: What is Kingsmills?
A:
i) A retirement home for old footballers
ii) A retired football ground (the old home of Inverness Thistle)
iii) A hotel to which footballers retire for refreshment

80)
Q. What is 'taking the shot'?
A:
i) Stepping up to take a penalty
ii) A heavy drinking session, regretted the following morning
iii) It's your turn ('my shot') to do something

78) (Correct: i)
79) (Correct: all)
80) (Correct: all)

81)
Q: What in Inverness is 'durbs'?
A:
i) A useful X-word anagram of 'burds'
ii) A complete waste of time, and known as 'marbles' in the Lowlands
iii) A good excuse for belting a ten-year-old school swot you don't like

82)
Q. What is a bogie?
A:
i) A golf hole played in one shot over par
ii) What wee boys extract from their noses and eat
ii) A bairn's cart made from pram wheels, old wood and no brakes

81) (Correct: all)
82) (Correct: all)

Cheuchter Top Ten: 1

Kessock Ferry Blues

I doubt that any serious cheuchter music lover, if one could be found, would question the deserved premier position of this blues number. It was first performed at the Inverness Royal Academy Folk Club in 1968 and has been a folk club staple number ever since. The song's authorship is currently under dispute, but it seems that the verses were written by three different people so it's difficult to claim copyright. All folk songs should be in the public domain anyway so, if you'd like the full version containing all the verses, then contact us on kessockbooks.com. The song celebrates the Kessock Ferry district of Inverness when it was regarded as the toughest area of the town, the 'Wild West of Inverness'

a) (E) Hard luck son (E7) it can't be helped
You went (A) down to the Ferry, (A7) you got skelped (E#dim: *fancy touch*)
(E) Right 'enuff, you got the (B7) Kessock Ferry Blues (E)... (B7).

b) (*chord structure as above*): The folks down there can treat you mean
Kick in your head or rupture your spleen
Right 'enuff, you got the Kessock Ferry Blues.

There are several other verses, all variations on the themes of urban alienation, class conflict, rampant hooliganism, blatant thievery and unashamed violence. These anti-social activities have now largely disappeared and moved to Dingwall, but there remains a slight air of menace round the place, particularly when Clach FC are beaten, a not uncommon occurrence. This song is a celebration of the Inverness of yore.

Highland Characters: Tallest Man in History

Angus MacAskill was born in 1825 on the the Isle of Berneray in the Outer Hebrides. One of ten children, Angus was so small as a baby that he was not expected to survive.

However, by the time he had reached 30 years old he had become a giant. At 7 feet 9 inches, with a chest measurement of 80 inches, shoulders 44 inches wide, and a weight of 425 pounds, it is hardly surprising that he was known as 'Giant MacAskill' or 'Black Angus'. The 1981 *Guinness Book of World Records* named him as the tallest man in recorded history. Surprisingly, given his remarkable size, his body was perfectly proportioned.

He lived in Stornoway for a few years before the Clearances forced him and his family to move to Cape Breton Island in Nova Scotia. By the age of 20 he was 7 feet 4 inches and was known by the largely Highland community, other Clearance victims, as 'Gille Mor' (Big Boy).

His demonstrations of strength were prodigious. He initially worked as a fisherman, and he could lift to his chest height a ship's anchor weighing 2,800 pounds. He single-handedly fitted a 40-feet-long mast into a schooner. He could also lift a fully-grown horse over a four-feet-high fence. He toured with PT Barnum's circus alongside Tom Thumb, and he was invited to tea with Queen Victoria, who apparently took something of a shine to the massive cheuchter.

He died in his sleep in 1863, his local paper commenting: 'his mild and gentle manner endeared him to all'. The 'Giant MacAskill' museum was opened in Nova Scotia and, in 1989, a similar museum was opened to Angus in Dunvegan in Skye. Why Dunvegan, where Angus had never visited? Local man Peter MacAskill established it as a memorial to a notable member of his clan, and it is only 30 miles from Angus's birthplace. A renovated, thatched-roof croft, it sits proudly today on Dunvegan Main Street.

83)
Q: What is the meaning of 'strath'?
A:
i) A flat valley running alongside a river through the mountains
ii) How a German with a lisp says 'strasse' ('street')
iii) The nickname for the Strathpeffer Pavilion, a ballroom notorious for music, drinking, fighting and fornicating in the 1960s

84)
Q: What is a 'mannie'?
A:
i) A hapless male Invernessian, usually called a 'wee mannie'
ii) A man employed as a nanny, therefore shorthand for 'male-nanny'
iii) A statue in Sutherland to the notorious first Duke of Sutherland

83) (Correct: all)
84) (Correct: all)

85)
Q: What is a 'wifie'?
A:
i) The female version of a 'mannie', and too old to be a 'lassie'
ii) A derogatory term for a hopeless 'mannie': 'ye wee wifie, ye'
iii) A wireless connection to the internet ('wi-fi')

86)
Q: What is a 'Highland Fling'?
A:
i) An extra-marital affair anywhere north of Perth
ii) A nickname for the 'traditional' 'tossing the caber'
iii) Yet another ridiculous type of 'Highland dance'

87)
Q: Who or what is a 'Weegie'?
A:
i) The lower-case version of the letter 'G'
ii) An inhabitant of Glasgow, a Saxon settlement in the Lowlands
iii) A weed-infected garden: 'thon garden's a bit weegie: tidy it up'

85) (Correct: i and ii)
86) (Correct: iii)
87) (Correct: ii)

Highland Characters: Charlie Kennedy

It is often a journalistic cliché to describe premature death as 'tragic', but in Charles Kennedy's case the word 'tragedy' is entirely appropriate. Charlie was a highly intelligent, affable and entertaining man, and his sudden death at the age of 55 shocked many people, particularly in the Highlands.

Born in Inverness, Charlie was educated at Lochaber High School, Fort William, and the University of Glasgow. A consummate politician, he was elected in 1983 to the House of Commons initially to serve the SDP and, after the party's merger with the Liberals to form the Liberal Democrats, he continued to serve the Ross, Skye and Lochaber constituency. He was, at 23, the youngest sitting MP in Parliament, and he served the constituency for a period of 32 years, becoming in 1999 for four years the Leader of the Lib Dems.

A much-respected and admired politician, he substantially increased his party's vote and he led the Lib Dems in his and the party's opposition to the Iraq War. In 2006 he admitted to an alcohol problem and to having received treatment, and he resigned his leadership. However, he retained his seat and after the 2010 General Election he voted against Nick Clegg's decision to form a coalition with the Tories. In 2008 he was voted Rector of the University of Glasgow.

In the May 2015 General Election, this popular figure lost his seat to the SNP by 5,000 votes, having retained the seat by a margin of 13,000 at the Election five years previously. He was an unfortunate victim of the unprecedented national swing to the SNP which, in his constituency, was over 25%. One month later, on 1 June 2015, he was found dead at his home in Fort William, having succumbed to a haemorrhage apparently linked to his alcohol abuse.

He was constantly in demand on the TV, his charismatic, cheerful personality leading to the nickname 'Chatshow Charlie'. He was in many ways a larger-than-life character, but he never forgot his background as a Highlander. His common touch, compassion and undoubted political talents generated a sense of loyalty, and he had many lasting friendships, often with politicians from the other political parties. This was much in evidence in the obituaries written by politicians across party divides. Charlie's death was a great loss to all his friends, constituents and everyone who valued genuine commitment and sincerity in British public life and politics.

88)
Q: What do you call a cheuchter from Dingwall wearing a collar and tie?
A:
i) Sir
ii) Pretentious
iii) The accused

89)
Q: If you told a resident of Invergordon that it was the arsehole of the Highlands, how would they reply?
A:
i) With a Gallic shrug
ii) 'You've obviously never been to Alness'
iii) 'Aye, but I'm just passing through'

90)
Q: What is Dunrobin?
A:
i) An extravagant, fairy-tale chateau built by the main architect of the Highland Clearances
ii) The stately, family home of the Dukes of Sutherland
iii) A retirement home for a man (the first Duke, whose statue on Ben Bragghie is called 'The Mannie') who robbed the poor to feed the rich

88) (Correct: iii)
89) (Correct: ii or iii)
90) (Correct: all three)

91)
Q: What is the Brora Cultural Centre?
A:
i) An oxymoron
ii) A social club for retired Brora miners
iii) Where people from Brora go for STD treatment

92)
Q: What do you call someone from Wick?
A:
i) Dirty Weeker
ii) Dirdie Weeker
iii) Alan Whicker

93)
Q: What do you call someone from Thurso?
A:
i) Teenabowlie
ii) Al Bowlie
iii) Tina Turner

91) (Correct: i)
92) (Correct: ii 'dirdie' means 'busy' in the local dialect)
93) (Correct: i)

94)
Q: What are the Clava Cairns?
A:
i) Celtic-Goth rock band from Kitarlity
ii) Cockney rhyming slang for 'bairns'
iii) Bronze Age chamber site near Culloden

95)
Q: What is a 'scaffie'?
A:
i) Reggae dance evening (deriving from 'ska')
iii) Inverness Council cleansing operative
iii) French for Nescafe ('scaffée')

96)
Q: What is meant by 'shinty'?
A:
i) Japanese soft drink ('Shin-Tea')
ii) Mis-spelling of 'shifty'
iii) Dangerously aggressive cheuchter sport

97)
Q: What is the Dark Island?
A:
i) Roundabout in Nairn with no street lamps
ii) The Black Isle
iii) Benbecula

94) (Correct: iii)
95) (Correct: ii)
96) (Correct: iii)
97) (Correct: iii)

98) Q: Who was Edward Pine Coffin?
A:
i) Undertaker to the Wick gentry
ii) English aristocrat who helped crofters in 1846/47 potato famine
iii) Lumberjack from Helmsdale

99)
Q: From what would one normally drink whisky?
A:
i) Small, clear glass
ii) Dainty china teacup
iii) Large dirty wooden bucket

100)
Q: What is Kessock Books?
A:
i) Library in Fortrose devoted to writings of 6th-century St Cessoc
ii) Password for admission into Dingwall's finest brothel
iii) Bunch of Invernessians enjoying themselves

98) (Correct: ii)
99) (Correct: iii)
100) (Correct: What do you think)

KESSOCK BOOKS

Kessock Books is a publishing company based in Inverness, the capital of the Highlands and Islands of Scotland.

We publish informative, entertaining, original and thought-provoking books and related publications on a wide variety of subjects relating primarily to the Highlands and Islands.

For our current list of publications refer to our website:

www.kessockbooks.com